FR

This book should be returned to any branch of the
Lancashire County Library on or before the date shown

0 5 MAY 2021

1 9 NOV 2021

OXFORD
UNIVERSITY PRESS

Floppy saw a toy rabbit.

"Poor old rabbit,"
said Floppy.

"Nobody wants it."

Floppy took it to Kipper.

"Poor old rabbit,"
said Kipper.

Kipper took it to Mum.

"Look at this rabbit,"
said Kipper.

"Nobody wants it."

"Look at this rabbit,"
said Mum.

Dad washed it.

Kipper brushed it.

Chip and Wilma mended it.

They all wanted it now.

Oh no!

"Poor old rabbit,"
said Kipper.

Talk about the story

Why do you think somebody has put the rabbit in the bin?

Why isn't it always safe to take toys out of the bin in the park?

Why did everybody want the rabbit at the end of the story?

What is your favourite toy? What would you do if it got old and torn?

A maze

Help Kipper to get to the rabbit.